Math Workout

D1621027

For Your Own Workout

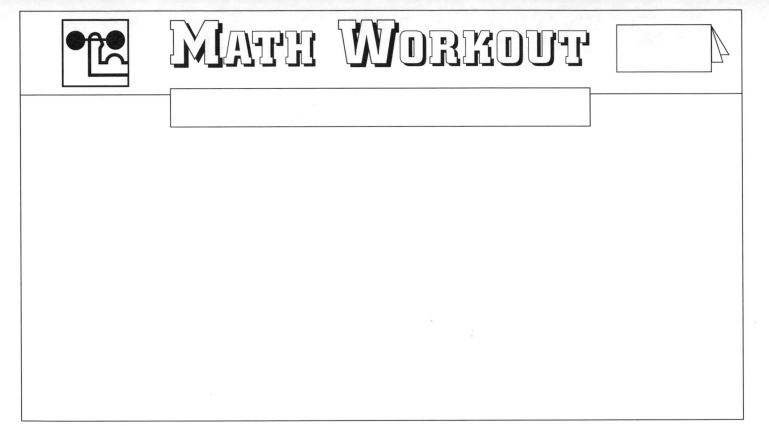

MATH WORKOUT

For Your Own Workout

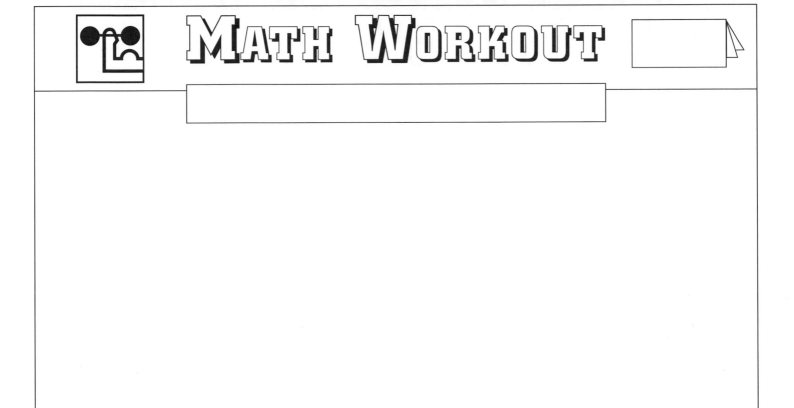

MATH WORKOUT

For Your Own Workout

MATH WORKOUT

MATH WORKOUT

MATH WORKOUT

MATH WORKOUT

For Your Own Workout

MATH WORKOUT

ESTIMATING AREA

PURPOSE: building estimation skills

MATERIALS: overhead projector, Activity Master 2, grid paper

Have a volunteer draw any triangle on grid paper or on the overhead projector. Have others estimate the area. Then have volunteers count to find the area. Use different shapes in subsequent experiences with this Workout.

UNIT 6 Exploring Fractional Parts

Math Workout  6-4

Adding And Subtracting Larger Numbers

Purpose: strengthening personal algorithms

Pose the following problem to the class: **Describe how you would add 759 + 468 and subtract 507 − 228.** Have students share their strategies and procedures for finding the answers. Discuss the different strategies and procedures. Use different numbers for both addition and subtraction in subsequent experiences with this Workout.

Math Workout 6-2

Division Facts

Purpose: maintaining division facts

Pose the following problem to the class: **Describe different ways you can share 24 counters evenly. Write a number sentence for each way.** As students give you different number sentences, write them on the chalkboard. Use different numbers in subsequent experiences with this Workout.

Math Workout 6-5

Find The Perimeter

PURPOSE: strengthening the concept of perimeter

Draw a rectangle on the chalkboard. Label its length 25 cm and its width 18 cm. Ask students to find the perimeter. Discuss students' methods for a solution. Use different numbers as well as a variety of geometric shapes in subsequent experiences with this Workout.

Find The Area

PURPOSE: strengthening the concept of area

Draw a square on the chalkboard. Label one side 13 cm. Then ask, **What is the area of this square?** Have a volunteer give the answer and explain how he or she got the answer. Make sure the class agrees with the answer given. Use different numbers and different shapes in subsequent experiences with this Workout.

Math Workout 7-1

Estimation Techniques

Purpose: developing estimation techniques

Write these calculations on the chalkboard: 63×5, 93×12. Have students work alone to write only the estimated products. Have students share their techniques for each problem. Discuss the different techniques as well as the fact that there may be more than one technique to arrive at the correct answer to each problem. Use different numbers in subsequent experiences with this Workout.

Math Workout

Patterns And Place Value

Purpose: strengthening the concept of place value

Pose this problem to the class: **Count by tens. Start with 323.** Have each student in turn give the next number in the pattern. Use different numbers for subsequent experiences with this Workout.

Math Workout 7-2

Division Facts

Purpose: maintaining division facts

Write these numbers on the chalkboard: 18, 24, 30, 36. Then ask, **Can each of these numbers be divided evenly by 2, 3, and 4? Explain.** Use different numbers with subsequent experiences with this Workout.

MATH WORKOUT

MULTIPLICATION

PURPOSE: developing the concept of multiplication

Write this problem on the chalkboard: 13×4. Then say, **Draw a picture to represent this problem. Then write the product.** Have several students come to the chalkboard to draw different pictures. Have them explain their pictures. Use different numbers in subsequent experiences with this Workout.

MATH WORKOUT

FRACTIONS

PURPOSE: building the meaning of fractions

Pose this problem to the class: **How many fractions can you name that are between 2 and 3?** Have students explain their answers. Allow them to draw pictures at the chalkboard if they want. Use different numbers in subsequent experiences with this Workout.

MATH WORKOUT

ESTIMATION TECHNIQUES

PURPOSE: developing estimation techniques

Write three calculation problems on the chalkboard: 578 + 821, 350 − 221, 375 + 118. Have students work alone to write only the estimated sum or difference. Have students share their techniques for each problem. Discuss the different techniques as well as the fact that there may be more than one correct answer. Use different problems in subsequent experiences with this Workout.

Math Workout 7-4

ADD AND SUBTRACT MONEY

PURPOSE: strengthening computation skills

Write these items and prices on the chalkboard: Sweater $24.95, Hat $5.99, Gloves $3.29, Scarf $7.00. Then pose this problem: **Martin bought two items. How much could he have spent?** Have different students find the sum of two items until you have exhausted all the possible combinations. Then ask questions such as, **How much more is the sweater than the scarf?** Use different amounts in subsequent experiences with this Workout.

MATH WORKOUT  5-2

DIVISION

PURPOSE: strengthening the concept of division

MATERIALS: overhead projector, 16 counters

Place 16 counters on the overhead projector. Then ask, **How would you share these among three people?** Have a student come to the overhead projector and manipulate the counters to show how they can be shared. Some students may say there is one left over while others may say that the leftover counter could be broken into equal parts. Use different numbers in subsequent experiences with this Workout.

Math Workout  7-5

ESTIMATING FRACTIONS

PURPOSE: developing estimation skills

Pose this problem to the class: **Name a fraction that is approximately 1.**
Discuss students' thinking. Ask students to explain how they know their
answers are correct. Use different numbers in subsequent experiences with this
Workout.

Math Workout 5-1

How Do You Multiply?

PURPOSE: building personal algorithms

Pose the following problem to the class: **Describe how you would multiply 3 × 76 and 5 × 46.** Have students describe their products. Discuss the different methods that students describe. Use different numbers in subsequent experiences with this Workout.

MATH WORKOUT 8-1

HOW DO YOU MULTIPLY?

PURPOSE: developing personal algorithms

Pose the following problem to the class: **Describe how you would multiply 5 × 63.** Have students describe the strategies and procedures they use. Discuss the different methods. Use different numbers in subsequent experiences with this Workout.

Math Workout

POLYGONS

PURPOSE: building spatial visualization

MATERIALS: overhead projector, Power Polygons

Place the three triangles on the overhead projector. Have students explain what is the same and what is different about the shapes. Use different Power Polygon pieces in subsequent experiences with this Workout.

MATH WORKOUT 8-2

DIVISION

PURPOSE: strengthening the concept of division

Pose this problem to the class: **56 students are entering the library. Each table has 6 chairs around it. How many tables will students need to use? How many will be at each table?** Have students explain how they know their answers are correct. Make sure the class agrees on the answer. Use different numbers in subsequent experiences with this Workout.

Math Workout 4-4

ADDITION AND SUBTRACTION

PURPOSE: strengthening computation skills

Pose the following problems to the class: **Describe how you would add 69 + 48 and subtract 86 – 29.** Have a student show his or her strategies and procedures for finding the answers. Invite other students to demonstrate different methods. Use different numbers for both addition and subtraction in subsequent experiences with this Workout.

Math Workout

Multiplication And Division

Purpose: strengthening computation skills

Pose this problem to the class: **An ad for mystery boxes of party favors states that there are 15–20 party favors in each box. How many boxes must you buy to be sure you will get 60 party favors?** Have students explain how they got their answers and how they know their answers are correct. Use different numbers in subsequent experiences with this Workout.

UNIT 8 **Combining Polygons**

Math Workout 4-3

PURPOSE: developing estimation techniques

Write these calculations on the chalkboard: $5.59 + $3.78, $7.00 – $3.78. Have students work alone to write only the estimated sum or difference. Discuss students' techniques as well as the fact that there can be more than one correct estimate. Use different numbers in subsequent experiences with this Workout.

MATH WORKOUT

ADDITION AND SUBTRACTION

PURPOSE: strengthening computation skills

Pose this problem to the class: **The coach has 500 school shirts for students. There are 386 left. How many have been handed out already?** Have students explain how they got their answers. Use different numbers for both addition and subtraction with subsequent experiences with this Workout.

Math Workout 4-2

Multiplication And Division Facts

Purpose: maintaining multiplication and division facts

Write the following calculation on the chalkboard: 6 × 8 = ? Then say, **Name the product and two related division facts.** Have students explain how they know that the sentences are related. Use different numbers in subsequent experiences with this Workout.

Math Workout

FRACTIONS AND DECIMALS

PURPOSE: building the relationship between fractions and decimals

MATERIALS: overhead projector, Activity Master 2, grid paper

Pose this problem to the class: **How can you show $\frac{2}{4}$ on this grid?** Have a student volunteer come to the overhead projector and shade the grid. Then ask students to describe the shaded grid in as many ways as they can. Discuss student responses. Use different numbers in subsequent experiences with this Workout.

MATH WORKOUT

ADDITION AND SUBTRACTION FACTS

PURPOSE: maintaining basic addition and subtraction facts

Pose the following problem to the class: **How many addition and subtraction sentences have an answer of 11?** As students give their answers, write them on the chalkboard. If students extend their thinking beyond basic facts, they may discover that there is an infinite set of number sentences that can be created with an answer of 11. Use different numbers in subsequent experiences with this Workout.

Math Workout 9-1

Find the Area

Purpose: strengthening the concept of area

Draw a rectangle on the chalkboard. Label the length 26 m and the width 5 m. Then say, **Some of this rectangular plot of land will be used for a garden. How many ways could you plant a garden of 65 square meters with whole meter sides. The garden must be kept as one continuous plot of land.** Have students draw pictures on the chalkboard to show how they would dissect the rectangle to show 65 square meters. (half the area of the rectangle) Use different numbers in subsequent experiences with this Workout.

PLACE VALUE

PURPOSE: strengthening the concept of place value

Pose the following problem to the class: **How many ways can you write the number 3,693?** Use what you know about place value to help. Use different numbers in subsequent experiences with this Workout.

Math Workout 9-2

Division Facts

Purpose: strengthening division facts

Pose this problem to the class: **Name all 2-digit numbers that can be divided by 7 evenly. Write a number sentence to show that your answer is correct.** Have students give a number and then write the number sentence on the chalkboard. Use different numbers in subsequent experiences with this Workout.

Math Workout

Mental Math Techniques

Purpose: strengthening mental math techniques

Write the following calculation on the chalkboard: $5 \times 9 + 4$. Ask a volunteer to explain how to find the answer. Then write $5 + 4 \times 9$ on the chalkboard. Ask, **Will this problem have the same answer?** Have students discuss why they think the answers will or will not be the same. Discuss the order of operations. Use different numbers in subsequent experiences with this Workout.

MATH WORKOUT 9-3

ESTIMATING PRODUCTS

PURPOSE: building estimation skills

Pose this problem to the class: **Two trucks are each delivering 35 cases to a supermarket. Each case has 24 cans. The supermarket is expecting a shipment of 1,800 cans. Is this a complete or partial shipment?** Have students describe the strategies, including estimation, that they used to solve the problem. Discuss the different strategies and whether an estimate is enough to answer the question. Use different numbers in subsequent experiences with this Workout.

Math Workout

Estimating Time

Purpose: strengthening estimation skills

Ask students to estimate how long it takes them to get to school. Have student volunteers give their estimates and explain how they determined their estimates. Ask students to give examples of other situations when they estimate time. Use different situations in subsequent experiences with this Workout.

MATH WORKOUT 9-4

MENTAL MATH

PURPOSE: strengthening mental math skills

Write the following calculation on the chalkboard: $6 + 9 \times 3$. Ask a student volunteer to explain how to find the answer. Then write $6 + 9 \div 3$ on the chalkboard. Ask, **Will this problem have the same answer?** Have students discuss why they think these answers will or will not be the same. Discuss the order of the operations. Use different numbers in subsequent experiences with this Workout.

Math Workout

MULTIPLICATION AND DIVISION

PURPOSE: strengthening the concept of multiplication and division

MATERIALS: overhead projector, Activity Master 2, grid paper

Shade a 5 by 6 rectangle on the grid. Ask, **What multiplication and division equations would describe this picture?** Have students give the sentences. Ask the class if they agree with the answers. Then ask, **How do you know the answers are correct?** Use different numbers with subsequent experiences with this Workout.

Math Workout

DECIMALS

PURPOSE: building the concept of decimals

MATERIALS: overhead projector, Activity Master 27, grid paper

Fill in 30 of the 100 squares of the grid. Place it on the overhead projector and ask, **How many different ways can you write a decimal for this?** Have a volunteer come to the overhead projector and write the decimals. Discuss with the class if all possible ways have been included. Use different numbers in subsequent experiences with this Workout.

MATH WORKOUT 3-1

ADDITION AND SUBTRACTION FACTS

PURPOSE: maintaining addition and subtraction facts

Write some addition facts where sums are 1 more than a double fact (for example, 4 + 4 is a double fact). Use 1 less in subsequent experiences with this Workout.

MATH WORKOUT 10-1

MULTIPLICATION

PURPOSE: strengthening computation skills

Write these computations on the chalkboard: $30 \times 8 = ?$, $(30 \times 4) + (30 \times 4) = ?$
Then say, **Explain how these are the same and how they are different. Do
they have the same product?** Discuss student responses. Then write this on the
chalkboard: $30 \times 8 = ?$, $(15 \times 4) + (15 \times 4) = ?$ Ask, **Do these have the same
product? Explain why or why not.** Discuss student responses. Use different
numbers in subsequent experiences with this Workout.

Math Workout 2-5

ORGANIZING DATA

PURPOSE: strengthening skills in representing data

Have each student secretly write a number from 1 to 10. Then draw a line plot, with the numbers 1 to 10, on the chalkboard. As each student gives you his or her chosen number, place an X above the appropriate number on the line plot. Discuss all conclusions the students can make using the completed line plot. Use different situations in subsequent experiences with this Workout.

MATH WORKOUT

MULTIPLICATION

PURPOSE: strengthening estimation skills

Write these calculation problems on the chalkboard: 38×43, 79×23, 49×52. Have students work alone to write only the estimated product. Have students share their techniques for each problem. Discuss different techniques. Use different problems in subsequent experiences with this Workout.

Math Workout

MENTAL MATH TECHNIQUES

PURPOSE: developing mental math techniques

Write three calculation problems on the chalkboard: 35 + 25, 100 − 89, 59 + 45. Have students work alone to find the sum or difference. Have students share their strategies and procedures for each. Use different numbers in subsequent experiences with this Workout.

Math Workout  10-3

READ A BAR GRAPH

PURPOSE: strengthening data analysis

MATERIALS: overhead projector, newspaper bar graph

Use a bar graph from a newspaper to make an overhead transparency. Have students discuss the graph and make calculations based on the graph. If the information on the graph is appropriate, ask questions about *mean, median,* and *mode.* Use different graphs in subsequent experiences with this Workout.

MATH WORKOUT

ESTIMATE SUMS AND DIFFERENCES

PURPOSE: building estimation skills

Pose this problem to the class: **Charles, Jenna, and Curt are bringing muffins to a bake sale. They promised to bring about 75 muffins. Charles has 25. Jenna has 28. Estimate how many Curt should bring.** Discuss the various estimation strategies students use to solve the problem. Also discuss that there may be more than one correct answer to this problem. Use different numbers and situations in subsequent experiences with this Workout.

Math Workout 10-4

Estimation Techniques

Purpose: developing estimation techniques

Write these calculation problems on the chalkboard: 5.9 + 6.8, 18.32 – 10.67, 4.73 + 5.29, 21.9 – 16.3. Have students work alone to write only the estimated sum or difference. Have students share their techniques for each problem. Discuss the different techniques. Use different problems in subsequent experiences with this Workout.

MATH WORKOUT 2-2

MULTIPLICATION AND DIVISION

PURPOSE: strengthening the concepts of multiplication and division

Draw four sets of 4 dots on the chalkboard with space between each set of dots. Then say, **Write as many different sentences as you can for this picture.** Elicit an addition, a multiplication, and a division sentence from students. Use different numbers in subsequent experiences with this Workout.

MATH WORKOUT 10-5

PATTERNS

PURPOSE: building algebraic thinking

Write this pattern on the chalkboard: 4, 8, 12, 16, __, __, __. Ask students to fill in the next three numbers (20, 24, 28) and describe how they decided what numbers to fill in. Use different patterns in subsequent experiences with this Workout.

Math Workout

ADDITION AND SUBTRACTION FACTS

PURPOSE: maintaining basic addition and subtraction facts

Ask students to write two related addition sentences and two related subtraction sentences using the numbers 8, 7, and 15. Have a volunteer write the sentences on the chalkboard. Make sure the class agrees with the answers. Use different numbers in subsequent experiences with this Workout.

Math Workout 11-1

How Do You Multiply?

PURPOSE: developing personal algorithms

Pose the following problem to the class: **Describe how you would multiply 25 × 46 and 38 × 24.** Have students describe the strategies and procedures they use. Discuss the different methods that students describe. Use different numbers in subsequent experiences with this Workout.

MATH WORKOUT 1-5

ESTIMATION SKILLS

PURPOSE: developing estimation strategies

Write three calculation problems on the chalkboard: 51 + 36, 85 − 28, 192 + 479. Have students work alone to write only the estimated sum or difference. Have students share their estimation strategies for estimating each problem. Discuss the different strategies as well as the fact that there may be more than one correct estimate to each problem. Use different problems in subsequent experiences with this Workout.

Math Workout 11-2

Division

Purpose: strengthening the concept of division

Pose this problem to the class: **There are 26 students. Each student should get one can of juice. How many 6-packs of juice do you need to buy?** Discuss the various methods that students used to solve the problem. Make sure students can explain why their answers are correct. Use different numbers in subsequent experiences with this Workout.

Math Workout

TIME

PURPOSE: strengthening time skills

Pose this problem to the class: **Your music lessons are 45 minutes long. It is 15 minutes from your house to the music teacher's house. If you leave home at 4:00, what time will you return home?** Have students describe how they got their answers. Discuss the various methods. Use different times in subsequent experiences with this Workout.

Math Workout 11-3

Estimate The Perimeter

PURPOSE: building estimation skills

MATERIALS: overhead projector

Draw any polygon on the chalkboard or overhead projector. Give each side a dimension. Ask students to estimate the perimeter. Have students explain the estimation techniques they used to estimate the answer. Discuss why there is more than one possible correct estimate. Use different numbers in subsequent experiences with this Workout.

Math Workout

Adding And Subtracting Larger Numbers

Purpose: strengthening personal algorithms

Pose the following problems to the class: **Describe how you would add 58 + 87 and subtract 74 – 18.** Have students share strategies and procedures for finding the answers. Invite students to demonstrate other methods. Use different numbers for both addition and subtraction in subsequent experiences with this Workout.

Fractions And Decimals

Purpose: building the relationship between fractions and decimals

Materials: overhead projector

Draw a number line on the chalkboard or overhead projector. Divide the number line into ten equal parts. Label the end points 1 and 2. Write *decimals* above the number line and *fractions* below the number line. Have students take turns coming up to the chalkboard and writing either a fraction or a decimal on one of the parts. Make sure the class agrees on all the answers. Use different numbers in subsequent experiences with this Workout.

Math Workout

MULTIPLICATION AND DIVISION

PURPOSE: strengthening the concept of multiplication and division

Draw a 3 by 5 array of dots on the chalkboard. Ask, **What multiplication and division sentences can describe this array?** Use different numbers in subsequent experiences with this Workout.

Math Workout

Probability

Purpose: developing the concept of possible outcomes

Pose this situation: **There are 2 green apples, 2 red apples, and 2 yellow apples in a bag. Tell the likelihood of reaching in without looking and choosing two apples that are the same color. Use one of the phrases *very unlikely, unlikely, just as likely as unlikely, likely,* and *very likely* to describe the chances.** Have students explain their choices. Use different numbers and situations in subsequent experiences with this Workout.

Math Workout

Addition And Subtraction Facts

Purpose: maintaining basic addition and subtraction facts

Pose the following question to the class: **What is the difference of 9 minus 5?** Have a student tell the difference. Then ask, **What addition fact can you use to find this subtraction fact?** Use different numbers in subsequent experiences with this Workout.

ADDISON-WESLEY

QUEST 2000

EXPLORING MATHEMATICS

MATH WORKOUTS

5-Minute Exercises for Staying Fit in Math
▼ GRADE 4 ▼

 Addison-Wesley Publishing Company

Menlo Park, California • Reading, Massachusetts • New York • Don Mills, Ontario

Wokingham, England • Amsterdam • Bonn • Paris • Milan • Madrid • Sydney

Singapore • Tokyo • Seoul • Taipei • Mexico City • San Juan

Copyright © by Addison-Wesley Publishing Company, Inc.

Printed in the United States of America

ISBN 0-201-84054-0

2 3 4 5 6 7 8 9 10 -BX- 98 97 96 95 94